CAPED CRUSADER CLASSICS

JUDGE DREDD GRAPHIC PAPERBACKS

BAT✦MAN

and

ROBIN

TITAN ✦ BOOKS

THE CHARACTER OF BATMAN WAS CREATED BY

BATMAN AND ROBIN
ISBN 1 85286 091 X

Published by
Titan Books Ltd
58 St Giles High Street
London WC2H 8LH

First Titan Edition August 1988
10 9 8 7 6 5 4 3 2 1

Cover designed by Rian Hughes

Printed and bound in Great Britain by Cox & Wyman Ltd,
Reading, Berkshire.

The LEGEND of the

— WHO HE IS
AND HOW HE
CAME TO BE!

DAYS LATER, A CURIOUS AND STRANGE SCENE TAKES PLACE.

AND I SWEAR BY THE SPIRITS OF MY PARENTS TO AVENGE THEIR DEATHS BY SPENDING THE REST OF MY LIFE WARRING ON ALL CRIMINALS

AS THE YEARS PASS BRUCE WAYNE PREPARES HIMSELF FOR HIS CAREER. HE BECOMES A MASTER SCIENTIST.

ONE DAY IN GOTHAM CITY, AS *DR. PETER DRISCOLL, FAMED RESEARCH SCIENTIST,* WALKS TOWARD HIS LABORATORY...

UHHH... *TRIPPED!*

RISING A FEW MINUTES LATER, HE WANDERS AWAY IN A DAZE, LEAVING BEHIND A BOUND PACKAGE...

...AN ORDINARY LOOKING PACKAGE -- YET, IT CONTAINS *SUDDEN DEATH!*

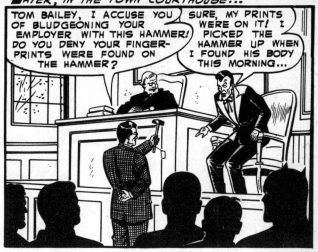

TOM BAILEY, I ACCUSE YOU OF BLUDGEONING YOUR EMPLOYER WITH THIS HAMMER! DO YOU DENY YOUR FINGERPRINTS WERE FOUND ON THE HAMMER?

SURE, MY PRINTS WERE ON IT! I PICKED THE HAMMER UP WHEN I FOUND HIS BODY THIS MORNING...

...BUT I NEVER SAW THAT HAMMER UNTIL I FOUND IT BESIDE HIS BODY! I'M INNOCENT, I TELL YOU!

ROBIN, THE TROUBLE HERE IS THAT THE POLICE DON'T REALIZE THAT'S A VERY SPECIAL KIND OF HAMMER!

THERE IT IS, **ROBIN** -- A **COOPER'S HAMMER,** USED IN MAKING BARRELS AND CASKS!

SOON, IN THE TOWN'S BARREL-MAKING FACTORY...

WE INTERRUPT OUR MUSIC FOR A SPECIAL ANNOUNCEMENT! **BATMAN** AND **ROBIN** DECLARE TOM BAILEY INNOCENT AND EXPECT TO ARREST THE REAL MURDERER AT ANY MOMENT!

WHAT? THEY'RE ONLY BLUFFING!

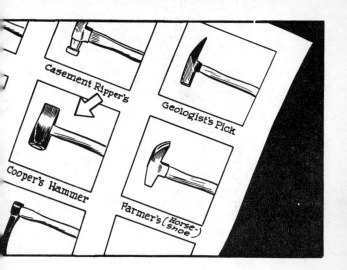

LATER, WITH THE INNOCENT MAN RELEASED, *BATMAN* EMBARKS ON THE NEXT LAP IN HIS RACE AGAINST DEATH...

SO FAR SO GOOD! BUT YOU'VE GOT TWO MORE TO GO!

NEXT ON THE LIST IS BRAD CARSON, THEN PAUL WADE!

WHEN BRAD CARSON'S TRAIL PROVES ELUSIVE, *BATMAN* WISELY CONSULTS THE ONE-TIME PAROLE OFFICER OF THE EX-CONVICT...

CARSON CALLS HIMSELF *CARTER* NOW! HE'S MOVED TO *CIVIC CITY*, A SMALL OIL REFINING TOWN!

THANKS! THAT'S ONLY A SHORT DRIVE FROM HERE! LET'S GO, *ROBIN!*

THAT WOULD MEAN RUIN FOR MY FAMILY IN THIS SMALL TOWN! I WON'T RISK THEIR HAPPINESS! I'M NOT GOING WITH YOU, AND THAT'S FINAL!

SUDDENLY, THE TOWN'S LOUDSPEAKER BLARES A WARNING...

ATTENTION! MITCH ROLLINS, JOE TYLER AND PAUL WADE, THE THREE ESCAPED CONVICTS FROM STATE PRISON, HAVE TAKEN REFUGE ATOP OUR LARGEST OIL TANK!

PAUL WADE! HE'S THE THIRD NAME ON OUR LIST! HE MUST HAVE GONE BACK TO A LIFE OF CRIME! WE MUST BRING HIM IN!

HASTILY, THEY DRIVE THE FAMED CANNON TO THE STORAGE TANK FIELD...

A MOMENT LATER, TWO HUMAN CANNON-BALLS ERUPT FROM THE FLAMING MUZZLE...

7

AFTERWARD, TWO CLOAKED FIGURES SURVEY THE RESCUED CITY...

GOSH, IT'S LUCKY YOU WERE ABLE TO *DISGUISE* YOURSELF AS WADE!

YES! HE WAS THE ONLY ONE OF THE THREE WHO WAS MY SIZE AND BUILD! I COULD NEVER HAVE MADE IT AS "BAILEY" OR "CARSON"!

STRANGE, ISN'T IT? BY SAVING THE LIFE OF OUR TOWN, WE ALSO GAVE THREE NEW LIVES TO BAILEY, CARSON AND WADE!

YES -- THEY, AND GOTHAM CITY, WILL BE ALL RIGHT FROM NOW ON!

THE END.

ONE FOGGY NIGHT, AS WEALTHY BRUCE WAYNE AND HIS YOUNG WARD, DICK GRAYSON, ARRIVE WITH OTHER SOCIALITES AT THE *GOTHAM CITY OPERA HOUSE...*

WOW! LOOK AT THAT COUPLE, BRUCE.. THOSE CRAZY CLOTHES THEY'RE WEARING! WHO ARE THEY?

THE BROMLEYS, DICK-- LAST OF AN OLD FAMILY THAT WENT PENNILESS YEARS AGO! THEY INSIST ON KEEPING UP A FRONT, THOUGH EVERYONE KNOWS THAT EVEN MRS. BROMLEY'S JEWELS ARE IMITATIONS!

SUDDENLY, FROM OUT OF THE THICK MIST...

EEEK!

HA, HA, HA!

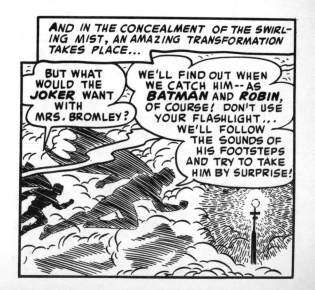

BUT JUST THEN...

CLUNK

OOPS! BUMPED INTO SOMETHING-- BUT I CAN'T TELL WHAT IT IS!

MAY AS WELL USE MY FLASH-LIGHT NOW, BATMAN! THE JOKER MUST'VE HEARD THAT NOISE ANY-HOW!

AND AS THE AMBER BEAM PIERCES THE FOG...

WHY--IT'S A MIRROR... A HEAVY GLASS MIRROR THE JOKER MUST'VE SET UP HERE TO CONFUSE ANYONE WHO CHASED HIM! COME ON-- LET'S CIRCLE AROUND IT!

ULP! W-WE'RE TWINS!

A MOMENT LATER...

LOOK! IT'S MRS. BROMLEY... BUT NO SIGN OF THE JOKER!

GUESS IT'S HOPELESS TRYING TO CATCH HIM IN THIS FOG! BESIDES-- WE'VE GOT TO ATTEND TO MRS. BROMLEY! HOPE SHE'S NOT HURT!

SHE'S ALL RIGHT... JUST FAINTED! BUT LOOK, ROBIN... SHE'S BEEN ROBBED OF ALL HER JEWELS! I GUESS THE JOKER DIDN'T KNOW THEY WERE PHONY-- ONLY IMITATIONS!

GUESS THE LAUGH IS ON THE JOKER THIS TIME!

LATER, AT POLICE COMMISSIONER GORDON'S OFFICE...

I'D BE A BUTTERFLY, HE SAID... AND WELL I MIGHT'VE BEEN, BECAUSE I THOUGHT I WAS LOSING MY MIND! HE *DIDN'T ROB THE BANK!* ALL HE TOOK WERE THOSE USELESS CHIPS OF WOOD, PAINTED TO LOOK LIKE GOLD COINS!

STRANGE... THE *JOKER* MUST'VE KNOWN THOSE COINS WEREN'T REAL, *BATMAN!*

THEN WHAT OF THOSE FAKE BROMLEY JEWELS HE STOLE LAST NIGHT? COULD HE HAVE KNOWN *THEY* WERE FAKES, TOO?

ALL I CAN SAY IS, IT LOOKS LIKE THE START OF A MAD *JOKER* SCHEME, COMMISSIONER-- BUT I CAN'T IMAGINE WHAT! WE'LL JUST HAVE TO WAIT FOR FURTHER DEVELOPMENTS!

AFTERWARD, IN THE SECRET BAT-CAVE...

IT'S NO USE! I'VE CHECKED ALL OUR TROPHIES OF OLD *JOKER* CRIMES, AND THERE'S NOTHING TO SUGGEST WHY HE'D BE STEALING WORTHLESS IMITATION VALUABLES!

HOPE WE FIND THE ANSWER SOON!

JOKER TRICKS TO ESCAPE LAW

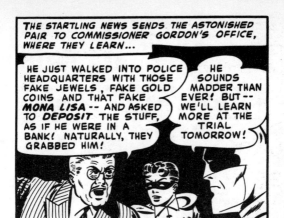

THE STARTLING NEWS SENDS THE ASTONISHED PAIR TO COMMISSIONER GORDON'S OFFICE, WHERE THEY LEARN...

HE JUST WALKED INTO POLICE HEADQUARTERS WITH THOSE FAKE JEWELS, FAKE GOLD COINS AND THAT FAKE *MONA LISA* -- AND ASKED TO *DEPOSIT* THE STUFF, AS IF HE WERE IN A BANK! NATURALLY, THEY GRABBED HIM!

HE SOUNDS MADDER THAN EVER! BUT-- WE'LL LEARN MORE AT THE TRIAL TOMORROW!

NEXT MORNING, IN A GOTHAM COURTROOM, AS A PSYCHIATRIST REPORTS ON HIS EXAMINATION OF THE *JOKER*...

THE PRISONER SUFFERS FROM *HEBOPHRENIC SCHIZOPHRENIA*... IN NON-MEDICAL LANGUAGE, AN INSANITY MARKED BY EXTREMELY FOOLISH BEHAVIOR! EVEN HIS TWISTED SENSE OF HUMOR WAS MERELY A SYMPTOM OF THIS INSANITY THAT'S NOW OVERCOME HIM!

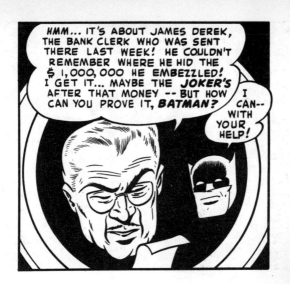

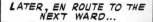

BUT SUDDENLY, AFTER A BRIEF WAIT BESIDE THE OPEN DOOR...

SAY, ARE-- *OOF!*

AND SECONDS LATER, AS THE DAZED CRIME FIGHTER OPENS HIS EYES...

HA-HA-HA-HA! INGENIOUS, THIS *BATMAN* OUTFIT I FOUND NEATLY PACKED UNDER YOUR SHIRT -- COMPLETE WITH UTILITY BELT AND RADIO! YOUR FALSE TIP ON DEREK'S HIDDEN WEALTH MADE ME SUSPICIOUS, BECAUSE LAST NIGHT DEREK REVEALED THE *REAL* HIDING PLACE BY TALKING IN HIS SLEEP!

BUT--IF IT WASN'T REALLY *BATMAN* I TIED UP--IT WASN'T *YOU* EITHER! THIS PLACE--HAS IT AFFECTED MY MIND? CAN *I* BE GOING CRAZY?

BUT WAIT!...THIS VENTILATOR! YOU COULD'VE SHOUTED THROUGH IT SO THAT YOUR VOICE WOULD EMERGE DOWNSTAIRS! AND, IN MY EXCITEMENT, I'M FORGETTING SOMETHING ELSE--THAT *BATMAN* ALWAYS WEARS A DISGUISE TO PROTECT HIS IDENTITY! YOU COULD'VE *REMOVED* YOUR DISGUISE!

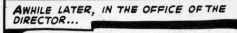

AWHILE LATER, IN THE OFFICE OF THE DIRECTOR...

THE *JOKER* DIDN'T KNOW THAT BY REMOVING MY UTILITY BELT, HE RADIOED AN AUTOMATIC DANGER SIGNAL TO *ROBIN!* I SHOUTED DOWN THE VENTILATOR, HOPING TO STALL THE *JOKER*-- AND, AS IT HAPPENED, I AWOKE THAT INMATE WHO THOUGHT HE WAS *BATMAN!*

I SAW HIM CLIMBING FROM HIS WARD WINDOW AS I APPROACHED, BUT HIS CLUMSINESS TOLD ME HE WASN'T--- COULDN'T--- BE THE REAL *BATMAN!* STILL, HE WAS HELPFUL!

HE'S ALSO A VERY LUCKY MAN! THE DOCTORS TELL ME THAT BLOW ON THE HEAD HAVE BROUGHT HIM BACK TO HIS SENSES!

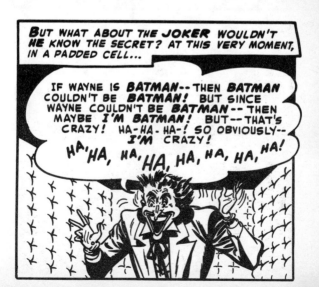

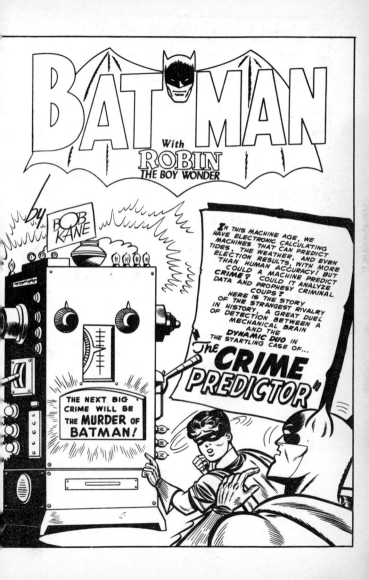

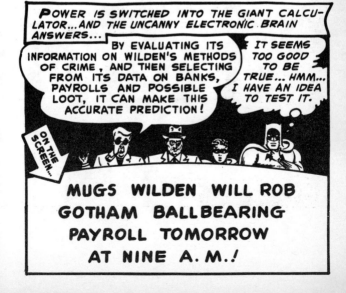

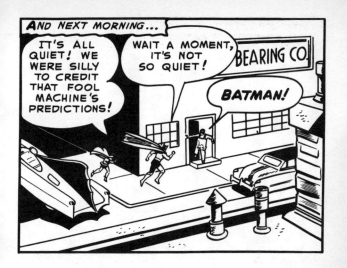

INSIDE THE FACTORY, WHERE BALL-BEARINGS ARE MADE FOR EVERYTHING FROM ROLLER SKATES TO HUGE MACHINES...

IT'S MUGS WILDEN, JUST AS THE *PREDICTOR* SAID... *OOPS!*

LEAPING TO ESCAPE A FALL, *BATMAN'S* TRAINED MUSCLES LIFT HIM OUT OF ONE DANGER INTO ANOTHER...

THAT WAS FAST, *BATMAN*...BUT SEE IF YOU CAN BEAT THIS!

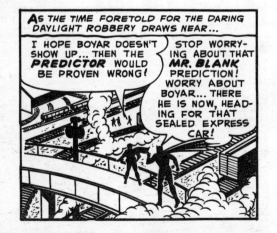

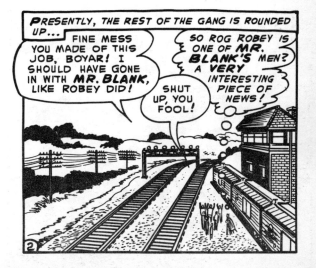

YES, WE MADE A NEW BOWLING BALL RECENTLY FOR A HAND WITH THOSE IDENTICAL MEASUREMENTS! MR. JON MARTIN, OF 44 PINE STREET!

THANKS! *ROBIN*, WE'RE CALLING ON "JON MARTIN"!

PRESENTLY, IN THE SECLUDED COTTAGE AT 44 PINE STREET...

BATMAN! HEY...YOU CAN'T DO THIS... I'M INNOCENT...

YOU'RE ON PAROLE YET CARRYING A GUN, ROBEY! THAT'LL BE ENOUGH FOR ANY COURT! TIE HIM UP WHILE I HOLD HIM, *ROBIN!*

I DON'T KNOW WHO *MR. BLANK* IS, BUT HE'S THE BIGGEST MAN IN CRIME NOW THAT WILDEN AND BOYAR ARE IN JAIL! WITH HIM AS MY BOSS, I'M NOT AFRAID OF YOU, *BATMAN!*

SO THAT'S ALL YOU'LL SAY? MAYBE WE CAN USE YOU TO FIND OUT MORE! LET ROBEY ALONE AND COME IN THE NEXT ROOM WITH ME, *ROBIN!*

BUT THE THIRD SALVAGE COMPANY **BATMAN** CALLS...

ROBEY? WHY DON'T YOU GET DOWN HERE? YOU KNOW THE BOSS IS HOLDING A BIG ORGANIZING MEETING TONIGHT!

I KNOW! I'LL GET RIGHT DOWN!

SO THE ACME SALVAGE COMPANY IS THE PLACE! AND IF I'M RIGHT, **MR. BLANK** IS THE BOSS HE MEANT! YES, I'LL BE AT THAT MEETING!

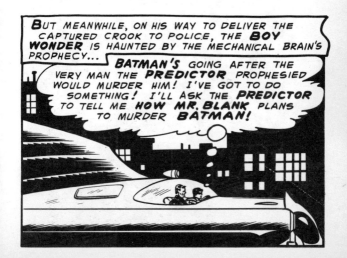

BUT MEANWHILE, ON HIS WAY TO DELIVER THE CAPTURED CROOK TO POLICE, THE **BOY WONDER** IS HAUNTED BY THE MECHANICAL BRAIN'S PROPHECY...

BATMAN'S GOING AFTER THE VERY MAN THE **PREDICTOR** PROPHESIED WOULD MURDER HIM! I'VE GOT TO DO SOMETHING! I'LL ASK THE **PREDICTOR** TO TELL ME **HOW MR. BLANK** PLANS TO MURDER **BATMAN!**

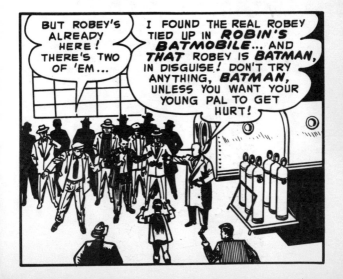

IT'S A SLIM CHANCE... BUT SOME OF THOSE CROOKS ARE SMOKING CIGARETTES, AND THAT'S OUR ONLY CHANCE!

GET IN THAT CHAMBER, YOU TWO!

PRESENTLY, AS THE CRIME-FIGHTERS ARE LOCKED INSIDE THE CHAMBER...

NO USE KEEPING THIS DISGUISE... IF WE GO OUT, IT'LL BE IN OUR OWN COSTUMES!

BATMAN, IT'S MY FAULT... I WAS WORRIED ABOUT THE PREDICTOR'S PROPHECY, AND THOUGHT THE MACHINE MIGHT HELP ME TO HELP YOU...

AND WHEN POLICE, DRAWN BY THE EXPLOSION, ARRIVE MOMENTS LATER...

YOU GOT **MR. BLANK!** BUT WHAT ABOUT DR. ARVIN?

DON'T WORRY ABOUT ARVIN, COMMISSIONER! HE'S...

...RIGHT HERE! FOR ARVIN HIMSELF WAS **MR. BLANK!** HIS **PREDICTOR** WAS A CLEVER PHONY, USED TO SCARE THE UNDERWORLD INTO ACCEPTING HIM AS BOSS! I REALIZED THAT WHEN HE BLACKMAILED ALL THESE CROOKS HERE BY THREATENING TO *"RELEASE"* ARVIN IF THEY DIDN'T OBEY HIM!

BUT HIS PREDICTIONS OF CRIMES DID COME TRUE!

The END

SOME HOURS AFTER THE NIGHT'S "LOCK-UP" AT THE STATE PRISON NEAR GOTHAM CITY...

I GOT PAST THE CELL BLOCK GUARDS! NOW I'LL HIDE IN THIS SHIPMENT OF BROOMS FROM THE PRISON FACTORY THAT'S GOIN' OUT TONIGHT!

PRESENTLY, IN A SUBURB OF GOTHAM...

FARNUM! WHY DID YOU COME HERE? YOU KNOW I TURNED YOU RACKET BOYS DOWN YEARS AGO! I MEANT IT THEN, AND I MEAN IT NOW-- I WANT NOTHING MORE TO DO WITH CROOKS!

TAKE IT EASY, DOC! UNLESS YOU WANT THIS TOWN TO KNOW ALL ABOUT... ER... YOUR PAST!

NOW I'M CONVINCED YOUR SECRET FOR CHANGING FINGERPRINTS IS ON THE LEVEL!

GOOD! WE CAN GET TO WORK! DOC BRICE WILL DO HALF THE JOB NOW-- CHANGE YOUR FACES! WHEN YOU TURN-OVER THE MONEY FROM THE JOBS I'VE PLANNED FOR YOU, HE'LL DO THE *HARD* PART-- CHANGE YOUR PRINTS!... THEN YOU'LL BE FREE MEN!

MEANWHILE, IN THE *BAT-CAVE*...

I'M STILL PUZZLED BY THAT MAN AT THE POLICE LECTURE, *ROBIN!* HE PRACTICALLY ADMITTED HE WAS FARNUM!

BUT YOU SAID SO MANY TIMES YOURSELF, *BATMAN*, FINGERPRINTS DON'T LIE! AND THAT MAN'S PRINTS WERE ENTIRELY DIFFERENT FROM FARNUM'S-- UNLESS HE CHANGED *THEM* AS WELL AS HIS FACE!

LATER, IN THE BAT-CAVE...

LATER, AT THE GOTHAM HOSPITAL...

LATER, IN THE **BAT-CAVE...**

I'D STUDIED FARNUM'S PRINTS SO LONG THAT I RECOGNIZED THEM WHEN I SAW HIS FINGERS MAGNIFIED BY THE LIQUID IN THE GLASS WHEN I HANDED IT TO HIM! THAT'S WHEN I FIGURED HIS GAME!

HERE ARE TWO SETS OF FARNUM'S PRINTS-- ONE SET MADE WHEN HE WAS FIRST ARRESTED YEARS AGO AND THE OTHER MADE WHEN WE RETURNED HIM TO PRISON YESTERDAY! BUT AS YOU SEE, *ROBIN*, THEY'RE EXACTLY THE SAME!

WHICH PROVES THAT CRIMINALS, LIKE LEOPARDS, CAN'T CHANGE THEIR "SPOTS"!

LEW FARNUM

LEW FARNUM

THE END

BATMAN GRAPHIC NOVELS AVAILABLE

Batman: The Dark Knight Returns
by Frank Miller
A grim look into Batman's dark future:
Frank Miller's brutal recreation of a
legend.
£7.95   Full colour

Batman: The Killing Joke
by Alan Moore and Brian Bolland
The final conflict between Batman and the
Joker — a terrifying look into violent
insanity by the author of *Watchmen*.
£1.95   Full colour

Batman: Year One
by Frank Miller and David Mazzucchelli
The first time. The first case. The first year.
The full story of Batman's yesterdays.
£5.25   Full colour

TITAN BOOKS